W0006723

MW01074077

Unsteady As She Goes

Battling Parkinson's Disease After Vietnam

LOU EISENBRANDT

Just keep moving.

Peace,
Lou

Deeds Publishing | Athens

Published by Deeds Publishing in Athens, GA
www.deedspublishing.com

Printed in The United States of America

Cover design by Mark Babcock.

ISBN 978-1-950794-71-3

Books are available in quantity for promotional or premium use. For information, email info@deedspublishing.com.

First Edition, 2021

10 9 8 7 6 5 4 3 2 1

I dedicate this book to my family—Jim, Jen, Matt, Gen, and Matt as well as to my grandchildren, Will and Emma, who have never known their grandmother without Parkinson's disease.

I am also remembering my fellow Vietnam veterans who are dealing with the after-effects of Agent Orange exposure. Whether afflicted with Parkinson's or some other disease, I honor you and wish you peace.

"Welcome home!"

Contents

Glossary

Bradykinesia — Slow movement

DBS — Deep Brain Stimulation. A surgical option for the treatment of Parkinson's

Dopamine — Chemical responsible for controlling movement, emotions, and feelings of pleasure and pain. In Parkinson's, the supply of dopamine is depleted

Dysphagia — Difficult swallowing

Dyskinesia — Abnormal involuntary movement of muscles

Dystonia — A disorder in which the muscles contract uncontrollably. The resulting abnormal posturing can be painful

Festination — Shuffling, making quick, short steps forward

Freezing — A temporary inability to move. The sensation that feet are stuck to the ground.

Levodopa — Medication most commonly used to control symptoms of Parkinson's

Micrographia — Small, compact handwriting

Movement disorder specialist — A neurologist with extra training in Parkinson's disease

Off time — Period when medication is not effective

On time — Period when medication is working

REM Sleep — Rapid Eye Movement sleep. Phase of sleep thought to involve storing dreams

Retropulsion — Quick, short steps backward. It may lead to falling

Visio-spatial issues — Difficulty detecting changes in amount of space surrounding an object

Foreword

In October 1969, after serving as an Army nurse at Walson Army Hospital at Ft Dix, New Jersey for nine months, I received orders for deployment to South Vietnam. I would spend the next year working, initially, on a medical ward and eventually in the emergency room of the 91st Evacuation Hospital in Chu Lai, located in the northern part of South Vietnam. I returned to the United States in October 1970 and began working as a civilian nurse at Fitzsimmons Army Hospital in Denver. In November of 1971, I married and moved to the Kansas City area to raise a family while still living with and making sense of my experiences in Vietnam. In 2002, while answering the phone, I noticed a slight hand tremor. In 2003, I was diagnosed with Parkinson's disease, and my whole world changed overnight.

Following my neurologist's advice, I began a regimen of medication, exercise, and diet. I also set myself on a path to learn as much as I could about the disease. Enlisting the help of others familiar with Parkinson's, I sought to live the best life that I could with this new challenge. In that effort, I continued to engage in projects that were important to me, including publicly speaking about my time in Vietnam, sharing images and information with students, civic groups, and veterans' organizations as I had for 40 years. I filed a successful claim with the Veterans' Administration in 2008, as Parkinson's disease is on their approved list of diseases resulting from exposure to Agent Orange.

My path has shifted since 2005, from learning as much as possible to sharing information about my life with Parkinson's, in order to support other people living with Parkinson's or caring for loved ones with the disease. Since my diagnosis, I have become involved with two organizations that offer support and guidance for those of us living with Parkinson's. Turning Point, located in the Kansas City area, and the Parkinson's Foundation, a national organization, both serve to meet the needs of people with this progressive condition.

In 2005, I signed up for my first class (on meditation) at Turning Point. After participating in various programs, I was asked to serve on their board. My involvement with Turning Point has continued for fifteen years and I am currently Chairman Emerita of the organization. For several years, until the restrictions imposed by COVID-19, I facilitated a class discussing the emotional aspects of life with Parkinson's.

My involvement with the Parkinson's Foundation began a few years ago when I was asked to speak about the personal challenges of living with the neurological condition. I was involved with the nationwide Women's Initiative sponsored by the Parkinson's Foundation, am a member of the People with Parkinson's Council, which advises the national organization and, with my husband, serve on the Heartland Mission and Outreach Committee of the Heartland Advisory Board of the Parkinson's Foundation. Currently, I am involved in efforts to bring more information about the disease to the veteran community across the country.

My first book, "Vietnam Nurse: Mending and Remembering", a memoir of my year in Vietnam during the war, was published in 2015. My goal in writing "Vietnam Nurse" was to inform a younger generation about the history of the Vietnam war. I also hoped to keep alive the memory of those who served in the war. This book picks up where "Vietnam Nurse" left off. In addition, I wrote this book to share my PD experience with others who are living with Parkinson's or know and care for someone who is, and to provide practical suggestions for managing the signs and symptoms of PD.

My hope is to show that it is possible to live a full and meaningful life with Parkinson's, and to provide tips for living one's best life, even in the face of daunting circumstances.

You Have Parkinson's Disease

I sat in stunned silence for a few seconds while my troubled brain tried to come to grips with what had just been said. Shock is the only way that I can describe my feelings when the neurologist gave me the news. As with any unexpected situation, when you receive bad health news, the first question that came to mind was "How?" and that was followed by "Why?" and "What is this disease all about?"

After those queries, I followed with, "Isn't that for old people?" The troubling image I conjured up was of someone stumbling, shuffling, bent over, and struggling to button his sleeve or thread her needle. Surely that couldn't be me. I was healthy; I had been a runner. I played tennis and had just taken up golf; my children were out of college and just beginning their new lives. Surely this was a mistake. Yes, I did have a hand tremor, which might be a sign that something was not quite right, but Parkinson's? There must be some mistake!

I left her office in a cloud of confusion, not sure what

to do next. I don't recall a lot about the next couple days. I do remember curling up on the couch in a fetal position as despair and depression washed over me. My thought process went something like this: I'm going to die in a couple years, I won't see my children married, I had dreamed of having grandchildren, and our traveling days are surely over. Why purchase anything new? I didn't need anything that was only going to be useful for a couple of years. I had no appetite for food, which had never happened before. I just wanted to be left alone to die in peace. I even, just for a few minutes, contemplated suicide. Fortunately, I dismissed that idea over the next three or four days.

It has often been said that time heals all wounds. I would add that time offers the opportunity to see a perceived wound more clearly. Once I faced up to the fact that this disease was going to be part of my future, I did decide that there probably was no good reason for me to keep my diagnosis a secret. I learned by the fourth day, post-diagnosis, when we gathered with my husband's brothers and their wives, that sharing the news was the best approach. The empathy and understanding from relatives were overwhelming. Sharing the news with family and friends definitely helped me get through those first few weeks as I dealt with this diagnosis and what would become a new adventure.

There was one other piece of my conversation with the neurologist, that day when I was diagnosed, that I really didn't consider to be that important at the time. Later, I would find it was crucial to my diagnosis and future plans.

When I inquired of Dr. B what could have led me to be diagnosed with Parkinson's, she had two responses. The first was that heredity may play a role in the development of the disease. I now know that as many as 12% of people with Parkinson's can trace a connection to their DNA. However, I had no family history of even a hint of the disease in my relatives. My mother, in the last couple years before her death, had a slight hand tremor when she got tired. The aging process surely was to blame. That certainly was not Parkinson's.

The other item that the doctor mentioned as a possible predisposing factor for the disease was exposure to herbicides and pesticides. When I informed her that I was an avid gardener and occasionally sprayed some concoction on weeds or dusted my roses to kill bugs, I remember her exact words about my concern. She said, "Lou, we are talking **large** amounts of spraying," opening her arms wide as she impressed upon me that a few puffs of rose dust were not the cause of my Parkinson's.

It would be another seven years before that information finally brought me to understanding what had been the trigger to develop Parkinson's. She indicated that many farmers are diagnosed with Parkinson's due to spraying their fields. I lived in a small town surrounded by farms, but still did not think that that could have been the cause for developing Parkinson's.

So here I was, a 56-year-old, retired nurse, full-time volunteer for several interests, recently having taken up golf and a life-long gardener with numerous plots of flowers and vegetables growing in my yard. My family and I enjoyed skiing in the mountains at least once a year. My husband and I traveled, as much as we could, to far-away places. We relaxed on St. John in the US Virgin Islands, set sail on numerous cruises, and explored Europe. I also made trips to the Far East, specifically to Vietnam where I had served during the war as an Army nurse in a field hospital in 1969 and 1970. In addition, South America and Africa were also on our travel schedule as we allowed nothing to slow us down. With this devastating diagnosis, I was certain that all those activities would be changing in the very near future.

Looking Back

Fortunately, I have been a writer since my high school days, keeping a journal or, as we referred to them then, a diary. The first one, that I faithfully wrote in every day, is from 1964, my senior year in high school. I still have it. It has a key to lock it, though a hairpin can easily release the lock. The purpose of the lock was to keep my brothers from reading my inner-most thoughts. There had been a fake amethyst "birthstone" on the cream-colored, padded plastic cover, but it had gone missing some time ago. A few years back, my sister and I went on a cruise together and I took with me that newly rediscovered diary. We read the thoughts of my teenage self and laughed until our sides ached. Alas, the journal that I kept from 2003-2004 when my Parkinson's diagnosis was new, is a bit more serious than my high school yearnings.

Several years have passed since I scrawled my feelings across those many lines early in my diagnosis. I had put thoughts on paper with abandon. I listed detailed medical notes but, of greater interest to me, was what I had to say about my feelings and emotions as I began to deal with the disease. In preparation for putting this book together, I spent several days rereading my journal notes from those first few weeks after I was diagnosed. I also read my journal from 2002, the year before I was diagnosed, the time that I spent wondering what was happening to my body. I knew something was wrong for more than a year before the neurologist officially confirmed what I had. I wrote about my friend Carol, the other soprano in a small group of us who sang for many years at our church. After a few months of my right-hand tremor, she finally said to me, "Lou, will you please see a doctor about that hand. I can't read the music when you hold it because it's bouncing all over the place."

In another entry, I read about the skiing vacation we took to Park City, Utah, a full year and a half before I was correctly diagnosed. I noted in my journal that I took the first fall that I'd had in nearly 10 years because "my leg was not happy and felt tired." A couple months later, I recorded the following, troublesome message, "My mood today is close to depression—causes are the weather, Bob (my brother-in-law)'s triple bypass surgery, the impending war (Iraq)." Was it really those things that were depressing me or was it another early symptom of the onset of Parkinson's disease? I suppose I never will know for sure.

The War

Growing up in a small town in southern Illinois, I decided, during my junior year in nursing school, in Alton, Illinois, that I would join the military for the opportunity to travel, see other parts of the world, and make excellent use of my nursing degree. So, I joined the Army before my senior year, graduated and took my state boards to become a *registered* nurse. After spending six weeks at Ft. Sam Houston in San Antonio, Texas for officers basic training, I packed up my new Rambler American four-door sedan and headed off to my first duty assignment, Walson Army Hospital at Fort Dix, New Jersey.

Nine months later, I received orders for Vietnam. I arrived in Binh Hoa on November 1, 1969 and was assigned to the 91st Evacuation Hospital in Chu Lai. For the next 12 months, I served at that facility in two different areas. The first three months, I was on a ward that treated GIs who were being hospitalized for reasons other than having been wounded. My patients were inflicted with illnesses such as malaria, hepatitis, intestinal parasites, and jungle rot (infected leg and foot sores as a result of wearing wet boots and socks for days on end). The patients were given blue hospital pajamas to wear during their stay and returned to their units once their conditions were treated. For most of the young men, to just have a bed with clean sheets to lay on was a special treat.

After three months in that area of the Quonset hut hospital, I was given the opportunity to move to the emergency room. I accepted and spent my remaining time in *Receiving and Emergency* (R&E), caring for the wounded and comforting the dying. The nurses worked 12-hour shifts, six days a week and occasionally, additional hours. When casualties arrived, triage was our first priority, to assess the seriousness and location of the wounds. Triage was critical in determining the extent of the injuries and in expediting treatment for each individual. After starting an IV, if one had not been started by a medic in the field, checking an airway, looking for bandages and tourniquets, we did what was needed to make certain we had not overlooked a hidden piece of shrapnel or source of bleeding.

To get a complete picture, we often cut off the fatigues of the newly arrived casualties. As the herbicide Agent Orange was widely used throughout South Vietnam, odds were quite good that those injured, brought from "the bush" had been exposed to the chemical. Simply being within a few feet of the contaminated residue from a well-worn set of fatigues was enough to possibly lead to contamination, resulting in illness many years later.

In addition to dealing with Agent Orange on the clothing of soldiers, the herbicide, which contained dioxin in addition to other chemicals, was also sprayed around the compound housing the hospital, living quarters, the PX, and other facilities. On occasion, I would leave the compound for areas in the surrounding countryside. For example, I accompanied a band making a visit to an LZ (Landing Zone) to entertain the grunts. Most of the LZs were created by clearing the land, using Agent Orange, to provide an area where helicopters might land, and tents could be set up for a bit of R&R for the guys in the bush.

A couple years ago, I located a US government document that specifically listed the locations and dates for spraying the herbicide. Some statistics suggest that over 10% of the country of South Vietnam, by the war's end, had been sprayed with Agent Orange. Other information indicates that the concentration of the herbicide used was 13 times the recommended rate for application by the US Department of Agriculture. If only the general public had known what devastating, long-term effects the use of this chemical would have on those of us who served. At the time, most of us did not have a clue.

The Imprint of War

The nighttime silence is troubling
Even the treefrogs have fallen silent
No neon flash of tracers.
No incoming, whistling overhead.

We gather around the worn Scrabble board
Balanced on a dented metal trash can.
A nurse and two corpsmen
Taking a break from work,
A bit of distraction from life around us.

But we are in the emergency room (R&E)
In a field hospital
In a war zone.

The quiet is temporary.
A crackling voice comes over the "squawk box" on the wall.
"Five minutes out. Two uniform sierra.
One sucking chest. One left amp at knee
One KIA in bag."

I prepare new charts to record the incoming wounded.
We ready ourselves to start IVs, cut off fatigues to assess wounds,
To stop bleeding, inject morphine, insert
chest tubes, adjust tourniquets.

This becomes routine. The chatter does not.
"Will I die?" "How is my buddy?" "Where is the Lieutenant?"
"How bad is my leg; can you save it?"
"Can't see out of my right eye. Will I lose it?"

Thoughts of folks left behind.
To some, I look like the girl back home;
Others worried that their sweetheart or wife
will not accept his broken body.

Do I lie to give comfort or speak the truth
And add to the pain?
For the dying soldier, the sound of the human voice
Matters more than the chosen words.

Fifty years hence, many memories are a blur
Names may be forgotten.
Yet the time spent in war
Leaves its imprint on the soul.

Returning to "The World"

After returning from Vietnam in October 1970, I set about leaving the war and its terrors behind to return to a more normal existence. Taking some time off, I joined a friend, also a Vietnam vet and nurse, for a road trip through the northwestern United States. For five weeks, we drove from Minneapolis to cities along the West Coast — Seattle, Portland, San Francisco, Los Angeles, and Las Vegas, each time staying with other nurses we had met in Vietnam. Our final stop was in Denver, Colorado where we applied for civil service nursing positions at Fitzsimmons Army Hospital. Our applications were accepted, and we returned to Denver to begin nursing in early January 1971.

One troubling health issue that followed me throughout those five weeks was a constant headache for which I took as much pain medication as I could. As it was November and December at the time, when we returned to our homes, I ultimately spent four days, including Christmas, in a local hospital. After undergoing a battery of neurological tests to determine the cause of my headaches, all the test results came back normal, and the headaches finally subsided. I still believe that I had picked up some virus that refused to leave my body in a timely manner. Despite the annoying headaches and some numbness in my legs, I was grateful for a safe return from the war and pleased to continue working in my profession. I doubt that these headaches had anything to do with my development of Parkinson's numerous years later. However, I suppose I will never know for certain.

You Survived

The shower of rockets at night
The heat and monsoons during the day
The fever and chills of malaria victims
The tears of the wounded; the green bags for the dead.

You survived ...
The pleas of the amputee
Moaning with phantom pain
The cries of injured children
Too young to understand; wanting only to be safe.

You survived ...
Staring in the eyes of the enemy
The loneliness without family nearby
Food in the mess hall, powdered eggs and liquid Jell-O
Sand in your face, on your sheets and your lips.

You survived ...
To return home, unbroken
To fly that Freedom Bird, unscarred.
You survived the war, though forever changed

By a silent villain called Agent Orange.

This next chapter in my nursing career was different from what I had done the previous year. At Fitzsimmons, I was assigned to a female medical ward which could not have been further from what I was used to. I was not accustomed to dealing with female patients who needed significantly more pampering than the seriously ill and wounded GIs that I had cared for in Vietnam. Their greatest concerns were making certain that they had bed clothes from home and thus did not have to wear the hospital gowns provided. It just felt very frivolous following our life and death nursing in Vietnam.

Had I remained at that hospital for more than six months, I would definitely have requested a change of assignments. I missed the adrenaline rush that came with emergency room nursing, enhanced by the challenges of doing such nursing in the middle of a war zone. I missed the close camaraderie of my fellow medical personnel. It was just such a different world from what I had experienced in Vietnam. However, not everything about those months at Fitzsimmons, was of little significance. For it was there that I met my future husband, just six months after I had begun work.

He had joined the Army Reserves, to avoid the draft, having graduated from law school. As there was only one opening remaining in a local reserve unit, he found himself assigned to a medical unit. Once a month he would spend Saturday working at a mental health clinic in our area. In addition, each summer for six years, his unit spent what was called "summer camp" at an Army medical facility somewhere across the country. In May 1971, that summer camp duty took him to Denver, more specifically to Fitzsimmons and more precisely to the floor where I was the charge nurse.

He invited me to dinner during his second week at the hospital and we proceeded to go out to dinner four nights in a row as well as having breakfast on the Saturday before he returned to Kansas City. After a month of phone calls, followed by one weekend in Kansas City with him, he proposed, and we were married November 20, 1971. I did, in fact, say goodbye to my hospital duties in the female medical ward in Denver, just not in the manner that I had assumed would take place. We celebrated our 50th anniversary in November of 2021.

Life Goes On

When I look back at the 18 months from October 1971 to April 1972, I am amazed at the monumental changes in my life during that period. Having returned from Vietnam in October 1970, I was out of the military, living in an apartment, and nursing in Denver. By April 1972, I had found love, married, moved to a different state, bought a house, and become mother to a St. Bernard puppy named Sasha. I tucked away my memories of my time in Vietnam, cataloged my slides, and mounted my photographs. I stayed connected to some of the medical staff that I had been especially close to at the 91st Evacuation Hospital, including Vietnamese colleagues. I even received cards from the Vietnamese nurse who worked at the hospital.

Back in the States, I moved on to the joys of motherhood with our daughter Jen being born in January 1973 and later, our son Matt, born in June 1975. I began volunteering with organizations that were close to my heart. In the 1970s, I taught prepared childbirth classes for a private organization called Childbirth Education Association or CEA. We educated expectant couples about pregnancy, labor, and delivery before hospitals started their own prenatal classes.

As a stay-at-home mom, I enjoyed sewing for myself and my children, as well as my husband. My one creation that didn't quite work for him was our matching plaid jumpsuits (it was the '70s after all). I took a class in working with stained glass and thoroughly enjoyed creating sun catchers and larger pieces. I even sold several framed, window-sized pieces. Following on my passion for meal preparation, I taught cooking to children for approximately eight years.

In the 1980s, I was looking for something more to do and worked as a travel agent for 10 years. I occasionally considered returning to nursing, but I knew it was going to have to be something with a very serious challenge following up on my combat experiences. Though surrounded by memorabilia and my old uniforms, fatigues, and other remnants of war, I didn't really spend much time thinking about my service.

That changed one day when a fifth-grade teacher asked me if I would speak to her students about my time in the war. I converted some of my slides into prints and put together an outline of what I might say to the students. I had been back from the war about 10 years prior and was not certain that the world was ready to start talking about Vietnam. I thought, however, students might be interested, having not yet formed an opinion about the war as their parents possibly had. I decided that sharing my story was the right thing to do.

As I was approached with increased frequency to share my story about Vietnam, I found that there was quite a bit of interest in revisiting the time period that we referred to as the Vietnam era. I also realized that many of my fellow Vietnam veterans were extremely uncomfortable talking about the time they had spent in the war. While the public may have referred to what took place in Vietnam during the '60s and '70s as a "conflict", those of us who had spent time in that country knew that this was not a conflict but rather war.

There was a time-period from the withdrawal of American forces in March 1973 until the late 1990s where the shame of losing the war forced many Vietnam vets to choose not to discuss the fact that they had served there. There were many people who blamed the loss of the war on the soldiers rather than on government leaders. During the war, returning soldiers faced discrimination, scorn, and insults. Many were mocked and physically attacked with cries of "baby killer!" In addition, many groups had organized marches opposing the war and those who were drafted to serve in that war.

Difficult Re-entry

As the country started to come to grips with some of the postwar issues that soldiers were dealing with, an increasing number of medical personnel as well as individual citizens came to the realization that there were many lingering effects that needed to be addressed as a result of being a soldier in Vietnam. Perhaps the malady that received the most attention early on was PTSD, post-traumatic stress disorder. This physical and psychological condition gradually makes its presence known with symptoms such as emotional outbursts, insomnia, depression, and anxiety. It appears that some veterans were unable to leave the war behind when they returned to their home countries or worldwide bases. It became apparent that, in addition to the physical wounds left by the Vietnam war, there were other factors that did not present outwardly, but clearly were after-effects of deployment to Vietnam.

It took somewhat longer for the medical field to discover that veterans were also suffering from diseases connected to the use of toxic materials during warfare. Gradually, conditions such as cancers, birth defects, heart conditions, and lung maladies were plaguing veterans, often several years after returning from Vietnam. After discussions and studies with researchers from several countries, the Veterans' Administration concluded that many of these conditions were a result of exposure to Agent Orange. This herbicide, whose main ingredient is dioxin, was routinely and widely sprayed over South Vietnam to destroy foliage and open areas in the jungle to better visualize the Vietcong and NVA (North Vietnamese Army) hiding places. While there were other toxic agents sprayed over Vietnam, Agent Orange was the most widely used and is the best known of the compounds. The clear liquid herbicide acquired its name from the barrels with orange markings in which it was stored. While the resulting devastating health effects of the use of Agent Orange were not immediate, fifty years later, we are discovering what those effects are. Should the topic of the use of Agent Orange come into conversation today, most Vietnam vets will simply shake their heads and tell you how many of their friends have been affected, in some way, by its use. In some situations, veterans will simply state that "Two years ago my buddy Joe died of Agent Orange." No further explanation is needed.

What Is This?

I remember the moment well. I picked up the receiver on our corded house phone to answer a call. Suddenly, with the faintest of movements, the receiver wiggled in my hand. It troubled me, but not enough to pursue medical attention. I assumed that perhaps I needed something to eat or that I was dealing with hidden stress. Over the next several months, my right hand continued to periodically have a mind of its own. The movement presented itself especially when I attempted to hold a book or newspaper in front of me to read. I was also aware that this movement increased when I was tired or fatigued. It wasn't until my friend begged me to "see someone" that I made an appointment with a neurologist. On September 23, 2003, I made the following journal entry: "Played nine holes with D____. Made appt with neurologist about hand tremor."

As often happens when you make an appointment with a physician, the time between your first phone call and your actual visit may be several months. In my case, I finally saw the neurologist in December 2003. I recall sitting on the examining table as he checked my reflexes, had me complete various neurological tests such as touching my finger to my nose with eyes closed, watching his finger as he moved it side to side in front of me without moving my head, opening and closing my hand and lastly, turning both hands palms up and then palms down as quickly as I could. As I recall, I didn't have a great deal of difficulty with any of those movements, but I did still have this tiny tremor.

After we completed the round of tests and discussed his upcoming skiing trip to Vail, he said to me, "Well, you don't have Parkinson's." When I asked him what I did have, his reply was one that I will never forget. "One part of your brain is aging faster than the rest of your brain." When I inquired as to what specific part of the brain that was, he didn't seem to have a clear answer. He instructed me to take Benadryl for my hand tremor but also prescribed Artane if the Benadryl didn't work or made me too sleepy. I headed home, prescription in hand, hoping that this malady was a temporary inconvenience.

I tried the Benadryl which, unfortunately, did make me sleepy, so I took it only sparingly. The tremor did not go away, so I started taking the Artane. After four days, I developed what I refer to as a "fuzzy brain." I was feeling lightheaded, unable to a concentrate, dizzy, and generally not with the program. I made a call to my primary care physician explaining what I was experiencing. His advice to me was to forget the Artane and just take the Benadryl if I needed it.

Over the next few months, other symptoms started to materialize. For example, when my husband and I would walk for exercise, he pointed out that my right arm was not swinging like it should. I quickly dismissed this as due to carrying my Walkman in my right hand when I worked out by myself. The second notable detail was that, on a couple occasions, I nearly tripped on an uneven section of the sidewalk. That was something that had not happened in the past.

As both my husband and I started to get more concerned about what was going on, several friends recommended that I see another neurologist who they were familiar with. They sang her praises and said she would be a perfect physician to see for a second opinion. After a few months of encouragement, I decided to call and schedule an appointment with this neurologist. Again, I was unable to get in to see her until July 2004. When I finally did, after she took me through the same tests that the previous neurologist had had me perform, I got the news. I did have Parkinson's disease.

While the first neurologist didn't use the P word, this neurologist thought differently. I debated whether to seek a third opinion to confirm the diagnosis. But this doctor had come highly recommended by friends, and she did not seem to waver from her diagnosis. I now know that there is no definitive test for Parkinson's in living humans. The only certain confirmation is in autopsy. I am not ready to have that test performed on me just yet! The diagnosis is generally made from signs and symptoms. This new neurologist gave me two bits of advice: "Exercise! Exercise! Exercise!" and

"Rest! Rest! Rest!" She also suggested that I learn as much as I could about Parkinson's, becoming my own advocate.

Her advice about exercising simply reinforced what I had been doing most of my life. Resting was going to be more of a challenge. I was not one to take a nap in the afternoon. She suggested that I simply take time to put my feet up and relax. While I did not feel the need to slow down for a few years, as my disease has progressed, fatigue has forced me to do so. Still, at the time, my brain struggled to comprehend the news that it had just received.

Shock and Awe

In an effort to look back at those first few days after being told that I was going to be living with Parkinson's, I recorded, in my still legible handwriting, exactly what was going through my mind at the time. I even made a list of my thoughts in the following journal entry:

"During the first 48 hours, had severe anxiety attack and depression.

1. Never see my daughter or son married
2. Never see grandchildren
3. Could not sleep at night
4. Wandered through the house blindly
5. Could not eat
6. Felt despair—no need to live."

Just saying the word Parkinson's was something that I could not bring myself to do, yet I encouraged my husband to share that word with everyone, if they inquired why I was shaking, crying, etc. After several days, I knew that, while not being able to voice my thoughts in person, I could put them into an email which I sent to most of our friends. I started hearing from them about family members and friends who had been living with Parkinson's for 20 years and were still active. I slowly realized that I was probably not going to die anytime soon.

At the time of my diagnosis, I had unrelated surgery and a week later was hospitalized with post-surgery blood clots. In my hometown in another state, my mother was dealing with the return of metastatic cancer. She would subsequently pass away four months later, in October 2004. Perhaps my death was not imminent, but still my world seemed to be crumbling around me.

Who Was this Dr. Parkinson Anyway?

Parkinson's disease is named for the English physician James Parkinson, who in 1817 published a comprehensive description titled *An Essay on the Shaking Palsy*. It received little attention for decades and was only given its current name in the 1870s by French neurologist Jean-Martin Charcot. His studies, between 1868 and 1881, became a landmark in the understanding of Parkinson's disease when he made the distinction between rigidity, weakness, and bradykinesia or slowed movements, as the disease progressed.

The symptoms now commonly associated with Parkinson's patients, tremors while at rest, postural stooping, and paralysis, were first described in 175 A.D. Some of the earliest treatments for PD involved plants of the mucuna family of tropical vines, some of which produce seeds now known to be rich in levodopa. Levodopa is a direct molecular precursor of the neurotransmitter dopamine.

PD Settles In

Once the initial shock following my diagnosis had passed, I moved rather quickly to come to grips with what would lie ahead. One of the very first bits of information that I came across was that the average age for the onset of Parkinson's is 60. An average range is from 55 to 61. Clearly, I was in the target group for Parkinson's. Those who are diagnosed prior to age 40, including Michael J. Fox, are considered to have early onset Parkinson's disease.

In an effort to educate myself and become my own advocate, I researched as much information as I could about Parkinson's on different websites. My husband went to a bookstore and brought home a factual book laying out what I might expect from this disease. It was helpful but distressing. It spoke of things such as "off time and on time." "Off time" being when your medication is not working; "on time" referring to when it is. It suggested setting an alarm on one's watch in order to know precisely when you had to take your next dose of medication.

It mentioned words like dyskinesias (random movements), freezing and dystonia (muscle contractions). It hinted about strange symptoms such as losing one's sense of smell, the voice growing softer with passing time, and frequent falling due to balance issues. How could one disease result in so many diverse symptoms and behavior? I began to understand why people who had been recently diagnosed would deny having the disease for as long as they could. It simply didn't make much sense.

I continued walking for exercise, making certain that my right arm was swinging as I walked. I found myself looking down at my feet rather than enjoying the scenery as I passed. It was important to see what I would be stepping on with my next forward movement. I also found that, should I want to take a closer look at something specific, I needed to stop, plant my feet, and then turn my head. That was the one thing that I learned quite quickly. It was simply not possible for me to stroll and look around at the same time. If I attempted to do so, I felt very unsteady on my feet. Individuals who text while walking scare me!

As days passed, other quirky symptoms began to materialize. I found that my handwriting, which had always been quite legible, seemed to grow smaller and tinier, with less clarity. There were times that I would not even be able to read my own handwriting, which I found to be quite distressing.

My PD Wants to Scream

What I don't need to hear…
Bummer!
Oh sh__!
That's too bad; now what do you do?
Don't they have drugs for that?
Do you shake?
I thought that was an old person's disease.
Is it a family thing?
The Pope died of that, didn't he?
I had an uncle with that, but he's dead now.

What I want to hear…
Where do you go from here?
How can I help?
Call me—ANYTIME!
You look terrific; I'd never suspect.
If you need help with the gardens, just let me know.
Here's dinner for tonight; I made a little extra.
Hang on to my arm; those steps might be slippery.

Don't tell me about your dead neighbor. Tell me
that he played golf until he was 80.
Don't stare at me when I'm rattling. Look
into my eyes and my body will calm.
Don't proclaim "You poor thing" or "God, that's the pits!"

Just offer your arm, give me a hug, hold my hand, and give me time.
Just be there — whenever!

Getting Ahead of Myself

My first follow-up visit to my new neurologist was four months after my initial appointment. As we caught up on my personal life events—my mother's death and memorial service in Illinois, disassembling my parents' home as well as auctioning the house and its remaining contents—I launched into my lengthy list of questions about Parkinson's. At some point, Dr. B calmly said to me, "Stop reading." She indicated that I might want to slow down my pursuit of the specific symptoms and treatments for Parkinson's. She suggested that I was reading way ahead of where I needed to be at this point in the disease, assuring me that some of the issues I was concerned with would not likely be occurring to me for many years to come. However, over the years, I have learned that for some individuals, the progression of the disease occurs more rapidly than for others.

Before beginning a regimen that included medication, I remember Dr B asking me if there was anything that helped my tremor, which was my biggest concern initially. I told her honestly, that having a bit of alcohol calmed my tremor. My husband and I had a glass of wine every evening with dinner, and she suggested that we continue to do so. In her words, "If wine helps, have it for dinner, lunch, even breakfast." I recall telling her that putting red wine on my Special K with red berries was probably not a good idea. She chuckled at that. We do continue having that glass of wine with dinner, though it would take a lot more than one glass to disguise my tremor nineteen years later.

Several months after she diagnosed my Parkinson's, Dr. B asked if I would meet with another of her patients who, having recently moved to the area, was struggling with her disease. Dr. B's goal was for me to get the other woman involved in programs similar to those that I was taking part in. I told her I would be happy to meet and did join the lady a few days later, when she invited me to lunch at her house.

I remember the day so well, bright, sunny, quite warm. While I do not recall the lady's exact age, I believe that she was in her mid-50s, as I was, and a native of Brazil. When I arrived at the woman's house, the stove was covered with pots containing a variety of contents. As the pot containing an entire chicken stewing in boiling liquid bubbled away, she gave me a tour of her house, which I noticed was dark and shuttered. I observed her difficulty when climbing stairs and the hushed tone of her voice. She then proceeded to serve me a three-course lunch. While the food was quite tasty, watching her shuffle and struggle to neatly pour soda pop out of a two-liter bottle was distressing.

Nearing the end of the meal, she indicated that she had been living with Parkinson's for nine years and, when I reached my nine-year milestone, I would be dealing with the very issues that she was. By the time I left her house two hours later, I was so depressed that I cried most of the way home. While I was helping her, I also learned a valuable lesson from this experience. I will graciously chat with or meet anyone who has been newly diagnosed. However, given my response to the atmosphere in her home and heavy lunch, I now always meet in a cheery and well-lit public setting, a restaurant, library, or coffee shop when someone wants to share PD stories.

As I indicated, each of us living with the disease is unique. Managing your surroundings, including regular contact with positive acquaintances and settings is very important to your own well-being.

My journal entries that fall and winter speak of mental and emotional challenges that were relatively new to my daily living. As the weeks passed, I made several notes about feeling "blue" especially as we headed into the winter months. I continued to keep up my schedule, playing golf when the weather was nice, and finishing up the gardening as fall brought cooler days and nights.

One recurring theme in my journal entries was a sense of sadness. Specifically, these episodes were noted on days when it was gray and cloudy. We now know this as SAD, Seasonal Affective Disorder. Natural sunlight leads to the production of serotonin and dopamine. Because Parkinson's results from an ever-decreasing production of dopamine, the depression that I was experiencing had a direct connection to the lesser amount of sunlight as the days grew shorter. Along with the encroaching depression, I also documented a lack of energy and slight fatigue.

The lowering of my spirits and mood reached a bit of a crisis during the Christmas holiday season. In the last minutes of preparation for Christmas dinner, I dropped a measuring cup full of warm chicken broth, creating a serious cleanup task just as people were being seated. I burst into tears and proceeded to sob for some time. While everyone was most supportive and joined in cleaning up the mess, I could not stop crying. No amount of comforting seemed to help.

On December 28, six months after being diagnosed with Parkinson's in mid-July, my neurologist prescribed an antidepressant. I have been on mood elevating medication ever since. On a couple occasions over the years, my physician and I have experimented with decreasing or discontinuing such medication. In the two situations when this has been tried, I could feel the depression returning within a few days. I have decided to not alter what is working. There is no shame in treating depression just as you would treat allergies or hypertension or diabetes. It is an illness.

There are other practices that are very helpful when dealing with depression, such as exercise, time spent with good friends, meditation, and more. Experience and the passage of time has shown what has been most beneficial for me in keeping my psyche functioning properly.

The Secret Signs

In reflecting on the last 19 years, the characteristics of Parkinson's disease that have been most troublesome for me are those that are not necessarily visible to others. I have often read that it is difficult to live with Parkinson's and keep the disease a secret. Generally, it is a challenge to disguise tremor, stiffness (especially in your legs), and the shifting posture. It may be less of a challenge to hide depression and anxiety. Perhaps this is why the mental challenges associated with this disease get so much less attention than the physical symptoms. For myself, and many other Parkinson's sufferers, the mental challenges can be more crippling than the physical manifestations of the disease.

I have found, when addressing the issue of depression and anxiety, that even some of those living with the disease are surprised to know that there is a connection. Often one hears comments such as, "Oh I'm not depressed, I'm just a little tired." In fact, depression can display itself in several ways. Difficulty concentrating, apathy, excessive sleeping, or the inability to stay asleep at night can all be signs of depression. Apathy means a lack of enthusiasm such that one may find it hard to get excited about many things she/he previously found enjoyable.

Some experts describe the feeling as a decreased interest in life in general. This particular aspect of Parkinson's has been most frustrating for me. In my past life, if I saw something that needed to be done, I would take care of the issue in a timely manner. I was not a procrastinator. At this point in my journey, some days it is a challenge to do more than sit and stare at television or read a book. Engaging in an exercise activity requires even more enthusiasm that I find difficult to muster some days.

As I mentioned earlier, those of us with Parkinson's have a chemical depression because of our depleted supply of cells that make dopamine. It is no surprise that 50% to 75% of Parkinson's patients live with depression.

Anxiety is often associated with depression. While depression causes one to have less interest in day-to-day activities, anxiety tends to express itself as an overreaction to daily matters. My initial experience with anxiety was during those first few days after I was diagnosed. My anxiety was greatly due to fear and concern of the unknown, of the future. Other Parkinson's patients struggle with anxiety throughout the progression of their disease. Much of that anxiety is again due to the uncertainty of what lies ahead.

Unfortunately, both anxiety and depression can increase the physical manifestations of the disease. Both of these neurological challenges should be discussed with your physician or neurologist, or in meeting with a mental health professional like a counselor or therapist. Attempting to self-medicate, such as with drugs or alcohol, is never a good idea. Talk to your doc!

One other issue that I had to deal with early on was anxiety caused by crowds. I remember going to a children's store to purchase something for my newborn grandchild. I actually felt claustrophobic because there were so many shoppers. I had difficulty making up my mind what to choose. It was a very strange feeling that I had not experienced in the past and, fortunately, has subsided over the years. I have, however, continued to avoid certain situations such as shopping at huge "we-have-everything" stores!

Learning to Adjust

As the months and then years rolled by, I continued to keep myself busy with projects that I had been involved with for some time. I continued sewing, which was a passion of mine. Spending hours in my gardens and digging in the dirt delighted me. My husband and I traveled the world, including San Francisco, Canada, Peru, Vietnam, and the Galapagos. I did not feel any restrictions in terms of movement though I did not have the energy that I had had prior to my diagnosis. My right-hand tremor continued to be the most visible of my symptoms and eventually led my neurologist to prescribe medication beyond that glass of wine with a meal.

In addition to my antidepressant, Dr. B prescribed for me a medication that, at one time, was used for Parkinson's. Unfortunately, that specific drug did not get along well with my depression. I struggled for several months, not seeing any improvement in my tremor but definitely an increase in the depression.

Along with daily walking, in my search to lessen my symptoms, I also availed myself of services that were offered in the Kansas City area at a place called Turning Point. It is a nonprofit organization that offers informational classes and hands-on presentations on matters ranging from meditation to nutrition to yoga and resilience. Without cost to participants, it serves individuals and their families who are experiencing life-changing, long-term conditions. Having practiced tai chi for several years prior to my diagnosis, I decided to add yoga to my routine, which proved to be very beneficial. The positions and gentle movement served to keep my muscles fluid. It also helped ward off balance problems.

In time, as I found it increasingly difficult to get down on the floor, and even harder to get up, I moved on to yoga in chairs. The classes that I took at Turning Point helped me get through those early years when I did not know where else to turn.

After six years of living with the disease, I realized that I needed to see a different neurologist, one specializing in movement disorders such as Parkinson's. I felt that I needed a change, a move forward. Following a three-month wait to obtain an appointment, I met and became a patient of Dr. Raj Pahwa. What I was looking for at that time was someone who was extremely knowledgeable about the medications for the disease. He had that knowledge and has continued to treat me for the last 11 years. You must find a practitioner with whom you are comfortable and who can give you the best information to control the disease. If you have not yet found that person, get a second or even a third opinion. This is a long-term partnership. You must have trust in each other.

Confucius vs Pharmacia

I'm not sure that Confucius can get credit for acupuncture, but clearly the Chinese have known about the healing powers of this practice for centuries. I had never experienced acupuncture until I started being a client of Chris Powell in 2006. I heard about Chris when I attended a class that he led at Turning Point on acupuncture and Chinese herbs. I have always believed, even as someone with a medical background, that alternate methods of healing could supplement modern science. Over the years, from depression to tremor to muscle aches and pains, I have found relief from this ancient practice. In China, acupuncture is actually used, on occasion, as anesthesia for surgical procedures. I'm not quite ready to commit that completely to the use of acupuncture, but it certainly has helped me work through some of my challenges with Parkinson's.

In this year of 2021, there are many medications that can be prescribed for the treatment of Parkinson's. There is no medication that will cure the disease, but there are many treatment options from which to choose. I began taking Carbidopa/Levidopa (commercial name Sinumet), the "go to" medication for Parkinson's, 15 years ago. As with any medication, do not expect miracles. The benefits are generally not instantaneous, and one must be patient to allow the medication to slowly alleviate some of the symptoms. There are situations where certain individuals may find no benefit from the drugs, or maybe even have an allergy to certain medications. In addition, most of the medications come with some side effects. It is up to the individual to decide whether the benefits outweigh the disadvantages of taking a specific medication. Again, a knowledgeable neurologist is important in assisting one in making that decision.

For those living with Parkinson's who do not fare well on oral medication, there is further treatment that is available. There are patches and pumps for delivering medication, and even a form of brain surgery called Deep Brain Stimulation. Since none of these have been part of my living with Parkinson's to this point, I am going to refrain from going into too much detail. Simply stated, the patches and pumps work by getting dopamine into the body through means other than swallowing. Just recently, I have started using an inhaler to obtain quick relief during my "off" periods. It serves to bridge the gap between when my medicine quit working and my next dose. Surgery is required for the installation of a pump.

Deep Brain Stimulation (DBS) is becoming more widely used for those who find that medication is no longer controlling their symptoms. In this procedure, electrodes are placed in the brain and connected by wires under the skin to a battery powered stimulator. When turned on, electrical pulses are sent to block faulty nerve impulses. Some of the results of DBS have been proven to make a huge difference in the life of the patient.

In general, DBS is not effective in treating balance issues. This is another situation where you must consult with a movement specialist as this is very invasive and complex surgery. It requires more than one surgical procedure and several physician and hospital visits as follow-up. In addition, there are certain symptoms of Parkinson's that are not relieved by DBS.

The first thing that Dr. Pahwa did when I met him was to take me off the original medication that I had been on. He told me that it was an old medication, not used very often, and confirmed my observation that it was possibly worsening my depression. He encouraged me to stay on the Sinumet. Though I still dealt with some nausea when I took the Sinumet, I persevered. Within two weeks, my depression started to lift. My apathy slowly eased. I felt as though the cloud had moved on and I could think more clearly.

I remember how good it felt at the time. Over the past 11 years, there have been a few situations where my depression has reared its ugly head, but only for brief periods of time. The depression has often been as a side effect from a drug totally unrelated to Parkinson's. There are countless medications with different compositions for treating Parkinson's. You can get information through your doctor, or other reliable sources such as the Parkinson's Foundation, and the Michael J Fox Foundation.

What I Fear Will Not Go Away

A slip of the foot on uneven paths
That strange ache in my leg as I write

The face, uneven, like a one-eyed queen
Shaky limbs, showing the world my imperfections.

Thoughts meant to stir the soul to action,
Not yet in focus, needing to be recycled again and again

Love, not lost or lessened
Lust, buried deep, needing a GPS to locate it.

Fear this? Fear tomorrow's advancing demons?
Sure! But what's to be done?

Grab fear and uncertainty by whatever presents itself
Hang on till life is wrestled from its grasp.

Take its energy; change its direction
Turn it within; transform it to hope.

Keep advancing and leave fear to find a new home!

The Best Medicine

Do you remember the last time you shared a big belly laugh? One of those laughs that reaches down to your toes? An observation that I've made over the years is that we need to find situations that make us laugh. I include this in discussing Parkinson's because so many of the chemicals in our bodies that give us the ability to laugh are in short supply when you're living with Parkinson's. So often those overwhelming feelings of being happy are not sensed as deeply as they were when we were younger. I remember getting together with girlfriends. One of us would start to laugh which served as a spark, setting off a wildfire of laughter throughout the rest of the group. Laughter is indeed contagious.

I once took a class on laughter from someone who was supposedly an authority on the issue, though I am not certain what her credentials were to attain that title. She said that there are four things that have been proven scientifically to elevate our mood. One is exercise, which most of us are already aware of. The second one is chocolate; the third is sex or intimacy. According to her, the final one is laughter. It does not take very much laughter to spread the joy around. There is truth in the expression that "laughter is the best medicine."

When meeting someone who has just found out that I have Parkinson's, the most common response is, "Oh, I'm so sorry." I generally thank them and then use a bit of humor. Early on, someone asked me how I stay so thin. My response was, "I shake it off." I joke about drinking white wine at cocktail parties rather than red, because white doesn't leave as bad a stain if you spill it. Some years ago, there was an item being touted on television for exercise. They were hand weights that jiggled as you walked. They were somehow supposed to tone your muscles and build up your arms. I often joked that I did not need weights that jiggled, my whole body jiggled. I think that simply making light of your condition puts others around you at ease. They may even be interested in learning more about the signs and symptoms of the disease.

Laughter, good for the soul, mind, and the body.

Photographs

Visiting LZ with band

Fellow nurses in Emergency Room

My last day; 91st Evac in background

Emergency room

Our wedding November 20, 1971

Daughter's wedding—Jen and Matt

Son's wedding — Matt and Gen

Vn nurse Rosie Winkler Smith

Vn Nurse Becky Dylla

Sign seen upon returning to Vietnam in 2013

Safari in Africa

Taj Mahal in India

Machu Pichu, Peru

Kayaking in Alaska

Swinging bridge in Dominica

Zip-lining in Costa Rica

Golf in Hilton Head

Revisit to Vietnam 2014

Making the most of my broken nose on a Disney cruise

Broken nose was perfect for Pirates night on the ship

Coin Toss Captain KU Med and Chiefs recognize Parkinson's Disease

Representing people with PD with my neurologist, Dr Pahwa at Chiefs game

Veteran's Service dog named "Lou" in my honor

First book

Moving Day Parkinson's Foundation

Celebrating women veterans

Turning Point Garden

Photo of me at the Women's Vietnam Memorial near
the Vietnam Wall in Washington DC

Steady As She Goes

I began this personal account of Parkinson's with a discussion about the mental challenges for one simple reason. They are often the most frustrating aspect to those of us who are victims, yet rarely does anyone mention this "elephant in the room." I suppose it's because, at least in this country, we don't talk a lot about mental health in general and certainly depression falls within that category. The physical manifestations of Parkinson's are more difficult to camouflage, yet the mental and psychological components can be the more troubling for those of us who live with them.

Let us now turn our attention to some of the physical idiosyncrasies of living with Parkinson's. It is important to know that *no two patients are alike*. Just because you know someone with Parkinson's who has been living with it for as long as you have does not mean that you will mirror their patterns.

Tremor is probably the first physical symptom that comes to mind when one thinks about Parkinson's. When

I was growing up, I didn't personally know anyone with PD, but I remember talk of someone who had an aunt with "the shakes." There are numerous neurological conditions that manifest themselves through tremor. In general, Parkinson's tremor is one that occurs when the body is at rest. It seems to be most active if you're in a setting where you are watching TV, reading a book, or even sitting in a meeting. There is another tremor called essential tremor that displays itself when your body is active. It is possible to have both essential tremor and Parkinson's, which is a bit more challenging.

In most instances, tremor begins mainly on one side of the body. As the disease progresses, it eventually may spread to the other side as well. For many of us, tremor can also be the most annoying. Picture yourself walking across your family room floor carrying a glass of liquid. The odds of you getting to the other side without spilling some of it get less and less over time. The challenge presented by eating soup, small fruits like blueberries, even spaghetti, can be most annoying. After dinner, the floor underneath your chair might look as if a toddler was playing with food. Way too much of it ends up on the floor. While there are weighted utensils that can assist in steadying one's hand while eating, if food falls to the floor, a pet like a dog or cat comes in handy.

Reading a newspaper presents another challenge as one hand flails while trying to steady the paper. I suggest you find a seat next to a table where you can lay the paper down without having to follow the bouncing sentences. I find reading news online via a computer or portable device laid flat on a table to be helpful in that respect. A few other sketchy situations you might encounter include threading a needle, putting on make-up, or shaving, and fastening jewelry. Especially difficult in these technologically-savvy times is using more than one hand to type a text message without dealing with 26 extra "i"s in a row.

I have found over the years that dictating emails, text messages, text documents, and more is the way to go. As long as there isn't a lot of background noise, the dictation feature is a lifesaver. Proofreading is essential before hitting "send", regardless of your vocal or typing ability. As to putting on make-up, my method is to put on eyeliner as best I can and then remove half of it with a cotton swab. Of course, you can always give up on the make-up if you choose.

A simple solution to tremor, depending on your location and the event, is to sit on your hands. It can be done discreetly and serves as a quick temporary fix. Emotions, positive or negative, can exacerbate a tremor. I first realized this shortly after I was diagnosed and found myself in a movie theater. I have no memory of what the movie was, but there was an action-filled segment that got my attention. My right hand went crazy. My first concern was that I was rocking the entire row of seats in the theater, but my husband assured me he couldn't feel any movement. Still, it was annoying to me and by putting my right hand underneath my derriere it helped substantially until a calmer scene came on the screen. I still prefer watching movies at home and not having to deal with the peculiarities of PD at public theatres.

A Tortoise or a Hare

A very common lifestyle change that occurs in Parkinson's is called bradykinesia, a long word meaning slow movement. As I frequently tell friends and acquaintances, nothing in my life these days moves very quickly. In the case of bradykinesia, the word "slow" can describe many parts of your body. Your gait slows down, your arm movements slow down, and your thought processes may eventually slow down as well. For me, this did not occur until I had been living with Parkinson's for several years. Attempting to hurry only makes things worse and may lead to an increase in falls due to rushing or attempting to turn too quickly.

Ultimately, you may find yourself needing some walking aids, such as a cane or walker. I use a cane if I'm going to be in a large crowd of people. It improves my mobility and serves to let others know that I am a slow-moving vehicle. At this point, I have not yet needed to use the walker that I procured after having back surgery a year ago. It is waiting patiently in our bedroom for the day that my body calls it into action. My cane also serves to provide a respite for the back discomfort that I have been experiencing the last few years. It can act as a third arm to assist in getting up from a chair or even out of a car. I have a cane that folds up which is perfect for traveling. When not needed, it folds in three places and thus can be slipped into my carry-on luggage.

Stiffness of muscles and joints adds to the reason for moving more slowly. As your body becomes less flexible as Parkinson's progresses, overall movements naturally slow down. At times, I feel like I am the Tin Man from the Wizard of Oz with awkward limbs and creaking joints. I no longer feel graceful. Simple movements can result in discomfort and even pain. For me, following a routine of light stretching or chair yoga every few days can alleviate some of the need for pain medication. I've also found that a session with a massage therapist from time to time can be quite beneficial. A spa massage that one might get at a beauty salon could be adequate, however, a massage therapist would likely be more cognizant of what Parkinson's patients need. Many physical therapy departments in hospitals or medical centers have someone who is knowledgeable about therapeutic massage. You might also be able to locate someone who will come to you in your home if you would prefer. Whether such treatment will be covered by your insurance or Medicare is a factor you might need to consider.

All Thumbs

Another feature of Parkinson's that many of us have heard of is the decrease in fine motor skills. This includes actions such as buttoning buttons, zipping zippers, picking up coins, especially dimes, removing a credit card from one's wallet, or separating dollar bills from that same wallet. A male friend proclaimed one day, "What was I thinking, buying all these dress shirts with button-down collars. If my wife isn't around to help me, it adds a good 10 minutes to my dressing time?"

Some of my clasps on jewelry present such a challenge that it hardly seems worth the effort to get them around my neck or wrist. I will usually resort to asking my husband to help, but that requires him to get his reading glasses and for me to stand near a light so he can see what he's doing. As I said, sometimes it just isn't worth it.

On a personal note, I encounter this manual dexterity issue while taking part in one of my favorite activities, golf. I never gave much thought to some routine movements of the sport, such as digging a ball out of your pocket to put it on a tee. Fumbling around in my pocket for a ball and tee easily results in my pocket turning itself inside out. Then I push the tee into the ground only to find that my tremor has kicked in and the ball won't stay on that little tee. Once I hit, I need to get that club back in the bag. Should I put the ball into the little cup on the green, I then need to bend over and dig it out. Amazingly, I play with very tolerant people who will pick my ball out of the cup. Should I hit the ball into a sand trap, I find once again that I need assistance.

Twice, I have fallen trying to get out of a bunker because of the shifting of the sand under my feet. It's a balance issue that my husband and golfing friends take seriously. Someone else retrieves the ball and I drop it nearby. I know, some of you are questioning whether what I am doing is really playing golf. Others of you are wondering, "What is this woman complaining about? She is playing golf, how handicapped can she be? I wish that I could just pick my golf balls up out of the sand and put them in a different location." I am pointing out some of the adjustments that I have made in order to continue staying active. Think about activities that you have had to adjust in order to continue something you love. The important point is to remain as active as possible. I now know that there is a gadget that one can put on the putter handle to help you retrieve a ball. My husband just purchased one for me and I love it!

The Mysterious Shrinking Handwriting

One of the very curious early signs of Parkinson's is the effect that it has on one's handwriting. When I first experienced this, I thought that I was imagining the change I was seeing. My handwriting, which had been quite legible, gradually, over a few months' time, got smaller. Even though I tried to make larger letters, the more I wrote, the smaller the letters became. I didn't in any way believe that this could have anything to do with Parkinson's. Yet, I was not surprised when that was a question that my neurologist asked me. The medical term for this condition is micrographia. Experts say this occurs as a result of bradykinesia or slower movement which causes difficulty with repetitive action.

In speaking with other Parkinson's patients, nearly all of them have experienced this change. It can reach the point where you have difficulty reading your own written words. I have tried printing instead of using cursive figures, but it doesn't seem to make a lot of difference. I also found that the situation worsened if I was under pressure to sign something quickly, such as writing a check while standing in the checkout line at the grocery store. It seemed to me that just the act of someone watching me made my handwriting worse. I found myself, whenever possible, making out checks ahead of time. In so doing, all that I had to do was fill in the amount when I was in line. Admittedly, with current payment practices, we now are accustomed to using credit cards and not needing to sign one's name so that anyone could possibly read it.

As an author, I do continue to sign my books, but I do them in the privacy of my own home, simply adding an individual's name when requested. Having to sign more than a name, when there is a line of people waiting to purchase a book, is not advisable.

Another strange phenomenon that can occur while one is in the process of writing, is a generalized stiffness or even pain throughout the body during writing.

A writing issue, perhaps not thought of until recently, might present itself if you were needing to show ID and provide a matching signature, such as when voting. For those of us with Parkinson's, our signatures may not look the same from day to day. How distressing would it be to be denied the opportunity to vote because one's signatures did not all look the same?

An encouraging experience for me has been that my handwriting, while still not perfect, has improved over the last couple years. I must add the caveat though that, if someone is watching me carefully, all bets are off. I can think of a couple other things that I found I wasn't able to do right after I was diagnosed but that have come back over the years. One is stirring or beating something by hand. The first year that I was diagnosed, I had trouble getting a rhythm to using a fork and beating an egg. I know it sounds crazy, but I couldn't get my hand to go around and around like it needed to, in other words, perform a repetitive action. I would make some rudimentary stabs at beating the egg, but I'd end up with more egg outside the bowl than inside. That motion has slowly improved through the years.

I Don't Smell Anything, Do You?

In this era of the coronavirus pandemic, I found it quite interesting that one of the early signs of the coronavirus infection was that many people were experiencing the loss of their sense of smell. For those of us who have been diagnosed with Parkinson's, this is something that would not help us in deciding whether we were living with COVID-19. Many individuals diagnosed with Parkinson's experience a similar decreased sense of smell. While that may not sound like a big deal to most people, one can think of a few situations where it might even be potentially dangerous. For instance, what if a gas leak occurred in your home? A sense of smell would be important. We also use our sense of smell in many other ways, including checking on the freshness of food, sniffing a diaper that needs to be changed, or enjoying the smell of rain, the spring flowers, or buttered popcorn in a theater.

As many of you already know, when you cannot smell something edible, your taste buds do not work properly.

Someone who is a connoisseur of wine first enjoys the bouquet of the wine before tasting it. I chuckle to myself when, in a restaurant, my husband will say, "My wife will taste the wine." The server will pour a sip or two of wine in my glass. I'll put my nose to the glass, swirl the wine a bit, and then proceed to sip the sample. As the server waits, I can approve or disapprove of the wine. I play the part but, if the wine really was bad, I'm afraid that I could not be the one to make that decision. Of course, my palate is not that sensitive, and the wine would have to be pretty bad for me to turn my nose up and ask for a different bottle.

Fortunately, in my case, I seem to have less sensitivity to disagreeable odors than I do to sweet fragrances. Being more sensitive to the smell of rosemary and lavender is definitely preferable to the pungent aroma wafting from undiscovered puppy poop in the corner or the odor of locker room socks found in the bottom of the hamper. So, it's not all bad.

No Sweat

For much of my life, I had not worried about being over-heated. During the winter, my feet were always cold. For a trip to the grocery store, I needed to take a sweater with me to ward off a chill. I anticipated that perhaps my body temperature would change as I went through menopause, but assumed that after those changes, I would be finished with hot flashes. However, the last few years, when others would be complaining about the cold air-conditioning in the summertime, I would be quite comfortable. I did not give much thought when it first started happening, until I awoke one morning to find that my night shirt and underwear were wet. Being a woman of my age, I was concerned that perhaps incontinence was taking over my urinary system. As I've stated before, things do start malfunctioning when you reach that magical age of 70.

What I didn't realize was that my autonomic nervous system, the complicated network that controls the automatic functions in our body such as heart rate, blood pressure, and temperature control, was being affected by my lowered dopamine level. While this effect is most prominent during "off" times when your medications are not affecting your body, it could occur at any time. Because I was off my medication from bedtime until taking my first dose of levodopa/carbidopa in the morning, the sweating took place at night.

I recall once speaking to a group of women about living with Parkinson's that I mentioned the night sweats during my talk. At the end of the event, a woman came up to me and quietly said, "Thank you. I am having the same issue and I thought that I was having bladder issues as well." That's the thing about Parkinson's, there is much that doesn't make sense but can be attributed to living with the disease. Adding sweating to the inability to smell, can lead to embarrassing moments dealing with body odor. You might rely on a trusted friend or partner to give you an occasional sniff test if you are concerned.

Regularity

This is an issue with the gastrointestinal (G.I.) system.
You know, the word that your mother used for constipation. Many mothers, from far and wide, have embarrassed their children by asking, regardless of what is ailing them, "Are you regular?" (i.e., have you pooped?) That is usually followed by, "Have you been drinking enough water? Have you been eating your deep green leafy vegetables?" At least in my household growing up, constipation seemed to be at the base of every ailment.

In Parkinson's, there is a real connection between constipation and that diagnosis. Research continues to be done in this area, however, there is enough evidence to support the fact that constipation could be one of the early signs that an individual could be predisposed to developing Parkinson's.

In addition to the direct connection between PD and the G.I. system, other indirect issues can affect regularity. One of these is a decrease in physical activity as the body slows down. It's well-known that exercise is important for a healthy G.I. system. The ability to exercise decreases, as fatigue, stiffness, and balance issues increase. Dietary restrictions can also affect the bowel habits. Uncut greens in salads can present an eating challenge, especially for those who might experience difficulty swallowing.

Another factor to be considered is the effect of medications prescribed for Parkinson's and other conditions. Many antidepressants list constipation as one of the possible side effects. This is another area where one must decide whether the good that results from taking the medication outweighs the undesirable side effect.

Should you find yourself having to deal with constipation, speak with your neurologist or pharmacist for recommendations. It is best not to launch into a program of self-medicating because there are so many over the counter options available to treat this condition. After struggling with this condition for years, I just recently found the solution for myself. It was recommended by a pharmacist and, at least for the time being, has solved the problem. It is a vegetable-based powder that can be mixed with water or orange juice and taken every morning. There are several brands and it is available at most grocery stores. I wish I had known about it sooner.

A Night to Remember

When I was younger it seemed to me that the older people got, the less sleep they needed. I had a grandmother who used to get up at 5 o'clock in the morning to bake coffeecake and rolls. I have found this to not be true in my case. I am a night person and have always been. My brain functions much better later in the day than first thing in the morning. Parkinson's, however, brings a whole new realm of interesting situations involving sleep.

Much has been written about sleep disorders associated with a plethora of conditions and diseases. Parkinson's is in that group. Some individuals have difficulty going to sleep. Others drift off to sleep without a problem, but only sleep for three to four hours, finding themselves awake for the rest of the night. Still others have difficulty staying awake during the day. Obviously, there's no one solution for all these situations.

The important first step is to identify the cause of the sleep problem. For someone who has difficulty going to sleep, perhaps an adjustment in one's routine could help. As we age, we often find that naps in the afternoon are beneficial, but they can keep us from being tired at night. If you need a nap to get through the afternoon, I suggest making it a short nap and taking the nap before 4 P.M. A respite in the afternoon can counteract Parkinson's fatigue, but it can also interfere with bedtime, especially if you are an early-to-bed person.

Perhaps the reason that one has difficulty getting to sleep or goes to sleep quickly but then wakes up in a couple of hours, is pain or discomfort. Difficulty rolling over in bed, pain from getting out of bed for frequent trips to the bathroom to urinate during the night, or even nighttime tremors could be the cause of your discomfort. If any of these are the issue, taking pain medication before going to bed may help. Consult with your doctor or neurologist. There are slow-release medications that can quiet your body during the night as the medication slowly circulates through your system.

Some Parkinson's patients experience leg cramps during the night. These can be quite painful and most certainly interfere with sleep. Gently massaging the legs can ward off cramps. In lieu of taking medication, potassium, such as found in a banana, can help with the problem. Recently I read that drinking tonic water, which contains quinine, may help to decrease leg cramps. I knew there was a reason that drinking a gin and tonic was just what the doctor ordered.

One might encounter a condition called "restless leg syndrome." While not exclusively a nighttime occurrence, it often takes place as the body is finally at rest at the end of the day. The legs twitch and will not relax; thus, the rest of the body is unable to be calmed as well. Some medications used for Parkinson's are also helpful in dealing with restless leg syndrome. Again, communicate with your neurologist to get a recommendation.

Another category of fixes for insomnia are aids that make use of quieting techniques such as certain yoga poses, meditation, Jin Shin Jitsu, and programmed relaxation. Child's pose is a yoga posture that can relax the body and be helpful in calming the mind. As I mentioned earlier, if you are having difficulty getting down on the floor (or getting up), check out classes of chair yoga. Meditation, either with or without music, can also be very helpful. Freeing one's mind from the troubles of the day plays prominently in getting the body to relax as well. The practice of Jin Shin Jitsu, which has been described as acupuncture without needles, can serve to calm busy muscles. By placing the fingertips on various points on the body, one can increase personal energy to those specific areas. Programmed relaxation involves consciously visualizing each part of the body relaxing as you start from your forehead and move down to your feet. It's an ancient practice that I learned many years ago when I was a prepared childbirth instructor in the 1970s. It was very helpful during pregnancy, labor, and delivery for women seeking relaxation. It continues to be a useful practice to unwind from daily stress.

Some in the medical community have encouraged sufferers of insomnia to take low doses of melatonin. Again, a conversation with your physician is advised before starting any medication on your own. I know of instances where long distance travelers have taken the tablets to help them sleep on a flight so that they awaken refreshed when they arrive at their destination. I had not taken melatonin until very recently when it was recommended by a pharmacist to help calm my body which, in the last couple months, has started acting out during the night as I enter the stage of REM sleep.

The REM sleep issue began later in my life with Parkinson's, but others may experience this phenomenon early in their journey. Some cases have been reported before the person was officially diagnosed with Parkinson's. Essentially, the body begins to act out dreams, some quietly, some with a bit more volume. Included with the shouting or snoring, one can throw a punch, shout at an adversary, or even take to sleepwalking. While this may not disturb the person who's living with Parkinson's, one's bed partner must live with the uncertainty of not knowing whether he or she will get a full night's sleep. While the best solution may be separate beds in separate bedrooms, this is not always an option. When my pharmacist recommended melatonin to help reduce the number of shouting incidents, I decided it was worth a try and have found it to be effective on occasion. The real surprise in this aspect of Parkinson's is that I do not wake up but continue to sleep soundly. Unfortunately, my husband is the one who is awakened. Even if he nudges me and tells me that I am shouting, I usually reply with a simple answer, "I know ...", and then go on with my performance.

Ode to a Gin and Tonic

When temperatures rise
To a scorching degree
And my clothes turn
Dark with sweat,
My taste buds start
To demand relief
With a tall glass of something wet.

Water might work
It's healthy and cool
Refreshing and
Easily taken in,
But nothing I've found
Can quench the thirst
Like a tall glass of ice
Filled with tonic and gin.

Clink go the cubes
Covered with just enough gin
The bubbles providing the fizz.
A plump wedge of lime to give it that tang,
No finer a drink there is.

So now we learn that thirst aside,
There's reason more to drink
The quinine may help those with Parkinson's
A cause to celebrate, I think.

Hunchback of Notre Dame

The gentleman who hung out in the bell tower of the French cathedral had substantially worse posture than those of us living with Parkinson's. However, there is little doubt that one's ability to feel comfortable while standing erect is definitely compromised. I was not profoundly aware of my slowly changing posture until I passed a large store front window and glanced, as people often do, at my reflection. I was shocked at how far forward my shoulders were leaning, causing my rounded back. I felt that I was walking quite straight until I got a good look at my profile. It was at that time that I realized physical therapy was needed for me to "stand up straight", as my mother would often remind us kids. I was definitely not standing up straight.

I often find myself looking down, especially while walking, to make sure that my path is clear of obstacles. Even an elevated sidewalk slab is enough to cause me to trip. Working with a physical therapist can be very helpful in improving posture and balance.

Feeling unbalanced is another factor in my worsening posture. When I straighten my back, I often feel as though I am somewhat leaning backwards, which might trigger a fall. Indeed, I have fallen backwards, once into a rosebush, not a graceful or comfortable landing spot. Another fall, several years ago, caused me to land on my coccyx (tailbone) on a concrete steppingstone in my garden. Needless to say, the bruise that I suffered from that episode prevented me from wearing a bikini for some period of time!

Don't Let Me Fall

Don't let me fall
as a weary hiker might
trying to traverse a deep crevasse
between two peaks
on a shaky rope footbridge
caught in a gust of wind.

Don't let me fall
as I did that early morning in July
when the plane reached 10,000 feet
and I felt the rush of air in my face,
unless I'm strapped to
a billowing chute.

Don't let me fall
as a child could,
peering too closely
to glimpse who might live
in the depths of an old well.

But hold me tightly,
make me steady,
calm my tremors,
strengthen my step,
allay my fears

and above all else,
let my spirit soar!

Wait for Me!

While we are on the subject of posture and body movement, there is another quirky symptom of Parkinson's. It's simply called freezing. It can occur at any given moment and generally does not give a warning that your body is about to freeze. The type of stop action that we are discussing is not due to a cold environment. This is not a type of freezing that results from decreased body or room temperature. Once again, it is the decreased level of levodopa that is the cause of the sudden inactivity. You may find yourself moving along at a slow, steady pace and suddenly you simply stop moving and must make a deliberate decision to take action to continue on your way.

As a general rule, freezing is not one of the early signs of Parkinson's but tends to occur as the disease progresses. It may happen more frequently when you attempt to either make a tight turn or find yourself needing to step over something such as a threshold. For instance, going from a carpeted floor to a smooth hardwood floor can cause your body to stop as it adjusts to the change. The average person, not living with Parkinson's, gives barely any thought to that transition, but it will require some extra thinking if you are living with the disease.

There are various tips that can help you get through freezing episodes. A simple solution is to stop, if you have not already paused, plant both feet, take a deep breath, and count each step taken as one, two, three, and so forth. Counting your steps refocuses your mind on the movement at hand. It allows your brain to redirect its attention to moving forward. Taking an exaggerated larger step, as if you were attempting to step over an obstacle, can help maintain your balance. Shifting from one foot to the other can also be helpful. Instead of pivoting, when trying to make a tight turn, you might want to consider small steps. All of these suggestions can guard against falling, the ultimate goal for good health. As I said, this challenge generally comes later in the progression of the disease.

On occasion, I deal with a somewhat strange phenomenon which causes my normally slow gait to speed up. It usually happens if I'm up in the middle of the night to use the bathroom. While I pause on the edge of the bed before standing up and making my way to the toilet, I have sometimes found that my feet are moving much faster than they should. This uncontrollable, tiny step movement is called festination. It's a word that I had not heard until just recently. I would describe the movement as flutter feet, tiny steps taken very quickly. Because it is typical to take the last dose of carbidopa/levodopa at bedtime, rising in the middle of the night presents a challenge to the body that has been without medication for more than three or four hours. I have found that a couple of things help slow my movement and return me to a normal gait. One is to grab onto the moldings around the open doors which I encounter on my way. Simply the act of touching something that is stable will assist in resetting your body's movement. The second suggestion is to, once again, count steps. In both of these situations, what counting does is help me focus on exactly what I am doing. As I count, my steps fall in line.

A third scenario where I have found counting to be useful is when climbing stairs. I have many friends who have fallen, especially as we approach our senior years. When questioned, often the response is, "I wasn't paying attention to where I was walking." It is easy to become preoccupied while navigating our busy lives. Perhaps our thoughts are about tasks left unfinished, meals to prepare, or needing to check the calendar for your next doctor's visit. For someone living with Parkinson's, one must focus on the physical task at hand, even just to perform simple movements, such as climbing stairs. Allowing the mind to wander may distract you just enough to misjudge the next step. Whenever possible, make sure that you have a sturdy handrail or a friend's arm to help you navigate steps whether there are two or 20. Do not be shy about asking someone to hold your arm. You will immediately notice how much more stable you feel. You might also make a new friend.

Capturing My Good Side

Over the course of reading about the unique signs and symptoms of Parkinson's when I was first diagnosed, I came across one symptom that I thought was really strange. It's called the Parkinson's mask. The manner in which it exhibits itself is a split personality facial expression. Generally, as I mentioned earlier, one side of my body was more affected than the other at the start of the disease process. This is also true for the majority of those living with Parkinson's. For me, it was my right side. That resulted in the right side of my face having a mask-like appearance. When I would smile, the left side of my face looked quite normal, while the right side looked stiffer. For instance, the right side of my mouth would not go up into a smile. My right eye did not open as widely as my left. There were more age lines and wrinkles on my left side. I found myself checking this all out by standing in front of a mirror. Holding my hand to cover one side of my face, I compared it to the other side. Amazingly, I could tell a difference.

The first few times I mentioned this to someone else, they looked at me with a look that said, "I don't know what you're talking about." Apparently, only I noticed it at the very start of my Parkinson's journey. However, as time went on, it became quite apparent that half of my face was smiling, and the other half was trying to. Some time ago, I came across an advertisement for a T-shirt that read, "I AM smiling. I have Parkinson's."

This may not be terribly disturbing to most folks. Many people say that the average face is not totally symmetrical anyway. I am more aware of the unusual quality of my smile when I have a photo taken. If I can turn the left side of my face towards the camera more so than the right, I feel I've done the best that I can. Therefore, I smile with the biggest, cheesiest grin I can muster and practice smiling quite often to keep those muscles flexible. A worthy practice I have found.

This is another area where laughter can be of benefit. By opening your mouth and laughing loudly, you are exercising the muscles in your face. Recently though, during the coronavirus pandemic, the positive aspect of wearing a mask, aside from reducing the spread of the virus, was that my crooked smile no longer bothered me.

I Can't HEAR You

As individuals age, it is quite well known that hearing often decreases. In this era of increasingly smaller and smaller hearing aids, many of us are unaware of just how many of our friends are wearing hearing aids. When I was young, my grandfathers' hearing aids consisted of a battery pack about the size of a package of cigarettes which was usually worn in the shirt pocket with a white wire leading from the battery to a very visible earpiece. There were very few adjustments that could be made to those hearing aids. They often were not very effective, loud noises set them off and it was often debated whether they were useful. All of that has changed as hearing aids have become much more adjustable, smaller, and connected to Bluetooth.

In the case of Parkinson's, the hearing concern has less to do with the problem of hearing and more to do with the problem of speaking loudly enough to be heard. As the vocal cords stiffen with Parkinson's, one's voice tends to get softer. For those of us who are singers, or were singers, our vocal range can decrease rather dramatically. Personally, I went from a vocal range of three octaves to barely more than one. While the limited range of one's voice is annoying, it's not as inconvenient as losing the volume that so often occurs to those affected by Parkinson's. Many have difficulty making themselves understood. Often the volume of the voice is barely above a whisper. While this can be disconcerting for anyone, it is especially challenging for a person whose livelihood depends on the spoken word. Obviously, the more individuals in a room, the more difficult it becomes to project one's voice to be heard. Table talk at a dinner for two might not present a problem. Dinner for ten is another issue.

Often overlooked is the psychological ramifications of not being able to make oneself part of a group conversation. Individuals with compromised speech may worry that their opinion and comments are not being considered due to their inability to make a clear statement. I have found that speech problems resulting from Parkinson's are also a challenge to the caregiver or friends of the individual. Lip reading can help to clarify the speech of someone with a very soft voice. During the recent pandemic, which found most of us wearing facemasks, the ability to read lips has been seriously compromised.

There is much help in the form of vocal training, including exercises to strengthen the vocal cords. Some of the vocalizing that professional singers do each day can be helpful in warding off speech issues. Working to project the voice as far as one can without straining or pain can be a helpful practice. Speaking to the back row of the audience, in theater talk, is one exercise that will help. Another practical suggestion is to drink plenty of water and other liquids to keep the throat from drying out. Unfortunately, caffeinated liquids and alcohol do not fit in this category. Yelling and screaming both do more damage than good. If the air in your home is very dry, consider the use of a humidifier. When possible, avoid situations where you must speak over other individuals in a room in order to be heard.

Occasional episodes of acid reflux can also affect one's vocal cords and, as a result, speech as well. If frequent throat clearing is needed to make your voice be heard, one might pursue the advice of an ENT physician. The connection between reflux and voice quality is often overlooked. Once again, certain medications can affect the vocal cords. Lastly, resting the voice, just as you would any other muscle, is a wise thing to do. Remaining silent for a period of time can improve your voice. Who knows, you might just find yourself refraining from a remark that would have been best left unsaid anyway.

Down the Wrong Pipe

Who among us has, from time to time, taken something as small as a sip of water, felt that choking feeling, and proceeded to cough for the next five minutes? Usually someone will ask if that sip "went down the wrong pipe." The medical definition for this occurrence is a bit more complicated. Essentially, your epiglottis (the tiny flap of tissue that prevents food from going into your windpipe) did not close properly to prevent water or food from getting into your trachea and lungs. As with the rest of the body, muscles in the throat of a Parkinson's patient become more rigid and less flexible. This may not be disconcerting if it happens with a bit of water. However, if this occurs when eating a meal, choking can become a concern.

It is best to avoid large mouthfuls of food, especially meats and bread. Snack foods such as potato chips and tortilla chips may present challenges if not chewed sufficiently. Some people find that eating foods that are very spicy can lead to some distress as well. A simple solution to avoid choking is to eat more slowly. Since everything else in the body seems to slow with Parkinson's, pacing yourself when eating a meal seems like a natural thing to do. Rushing through a meal is not the best approach. And maybe leave the habanero salsa for someone else.

Occasionally an excess production of saliva can lead to drooling, which, of course, is not a welcome sight! While I have not had to deal with that unpleasant experience, I do find that, especially if I speak immediately after eating something, it's easy to expectorate. That's a big word for spitting, which is also not well received by others who have joined you for dinner. The best advice that I can offer is what every parent has taught each child to refrain from doing. Don't speak with your mouth full.

A final thought — if you find yourself taking a collection of pills during the course of the day, it might be wise to space them out and not attempt to swallow all of them at once.

Standing Up; Falling Down

Many Americans, as well as citizens of other countries, are concerned about high blood pressure, which appears to be on the rise throughout the world. In the case of Parkinson's, that is generally not a concern. As a matter fact, there are more likely to be issues with hypotension, or low blood pressure. Specifically, a particular type of low blood pressure can occur with Parkinson's. Orthostatic hypotension refers to the condition where the blood pressure drops when one goes from a sitting to a standing position. When you visit your neurologist's office, you may be told that your blood pressure will be taken twice, once while sitting followed in one minute by a second reading taken while standing. Should your pressure experience a significant drop when standing, this syndrome can lead to lightheadedness, fainting, and even falling. This condition may not necessarily require medication but simply a change in movement. Getting out of bed slowly, by sitting on the side of the bed before standing up, will definitely help the situation. In addition, making certain that you are well hydrated is important advice to avoid lightheadedness as well as increasing your overall good health.

Here is some general advice concerning your next visit to a physician. Roll from your back to your side, slowly lowering your legs to a sitting position before easing yourself down from the examining table. There can be a tendency to get up too quickly, thus increasing your chances of dizziness. As the expression goes, easy does it.

Because carbidopa-levodopa is not taken generally during the night, getting up to face the new day having been off your medications all night, can present new challenges. As the disease progresses, one might find that morning stiffness can be relieved by taking medication before getting out of bed. If you don't have an understanding bed partner who can get the medication for you, leaving a pill and small glass of water at your bedside to be taken before getting out of bed is helpful.

Intimacy and That
Three-letter Word

I can sense several of you already squirming in your seat, not necessarily from Parkinson's but, more likely, from the topic. Many of us grew up in an age when issues about intimacy and sexuality were not discussed. Somehow, we figured those things out on our own which was fine until the bodily function that used to work no longer does. Simply stated, the process of aging can cause challenges to how we deal with sexuality. When you add to the combination a chronic illness, such as Parkinson's, those changes are often magnified. Practices that easily brought about pleasure may be hampered by the change in your body chemistry due to decreased dopamine. There are other causes of a decrease in sexual desire such as side effects from medication like antidepressants, or discomfort due to muscle and joint pain. It is not my intention to go into specifics but merely to propose a bit of advice. The suggestion that I offer is to be patient with yourself and your partner. You also might talk with your physician or a therapist and discuss what is causing you concern. It is quite common with Parkinson's that your body is changing and not responding like it used to. Again, I suggest, patience.

Searching for My Sexual Self

Where the hell are you?!

Are you hiding under the bed, in the closet, behind the door?
Have you gone on vacation or permanently
relocated to the south of France?

I've looked everywhere, gone through our luggage,
searched the basement, peaked under the Turkish rug in
the entryway, even groped for you in the hot tub.

You used to be everywhere — the family room floor, the glassed-
in shower, the chaise lounge on the deck, and even that hot tub.

You rarely needed an incentive to make your presence
known — flowers, good wine, a tender touch, chocolate mousse.

So why can't I find you; where should I look? I tried Jin-
shin-Jitsu, the liver flow that someone suggested. It helped
with my acid reflux but hasn't brought you back.

My acupuncturist strategically places his needles,
but they only calm my tremors.

I've prayed to Saint Anthony, who helps with lost
items; apparently libidos are not his forte.

Yes, Parkinson's moved in and needed some space. I guess you decided there wasn't room for both of you. I just want to know…

Where the hell have you gone!

Being Grounded

For years, when I facilitated a class and spoke to concerned individuals about the challenges of Parkinson's, I always mentioned mobility changes. We covered the fact that
one might reach the point where getting around was not as
easy as it had been in the past. Often, with a chronic condition, certain elements come into play that could eventually
interfere with your freedom. We talked about adjusting to
using a cane or other device to help you move about more
easily. I would usually tell the listeners that it must be a real
mobility adjustment in one's life should driving privileges
be taken away. I have recently learned that it is one thing to
speak about this in a group setting, but it's a whole different
situation when it happens to you.

As the pandemic was becoming a reality in spring of
2020, I began having difficulties with judging distances
while driving. Without going into detail, on two occasions I
found myself making a left-hand turn into oncoming traffic
rather than staying with the flow of traffic that I was part of.

I was also experiencing challenges with pulling into parking spaces and getting the vehicle straight. I refer to this abnormality as a spatial issue, not sensing precisely where the vehicle was versus where I thought it was. In addition, we had moved to a new home with very narrow garage doors. Twice, while pulling into the garage, I scraped my car against the side of the garage door opening. The second time, the car needed work done to repair the damage. Shortly thereafter, my husband and children apparently had a conversation about revoking my driving privileges.

There were a few tears, I readily admit, but I knew that they were probably correct in asking me to give up my keys. It was not the loss of long-distance driving that bothered me, but the short trips to the grocery store or to buy a gift for someone's birthday that affected me the most. I would now have to rely on others to transport me to where I needed to go. I also felt that my reaction time was becoming longer than it had been. That aspect can be affected both by the aging process as well as dealing with Parkinson's. Fortunately, there are numerous options for one to pursue as a means of transportation. I have found that many friends have come forward to offer their services, especially if they happen to be going to the same place that I am. Two dear golfing friends vowed, from day one, to always pick me up when heading to the course. When asked what he is doing in his retirement, my husband will tell you that he "drives Ms. Lou." There are additional services available, such as ridesharing apps like Uber or Lyft, as well as volunteer services through churches or other community organizations. In hindsight, the decision to no longer drive was the right decision. It made sense to give up that privilege before having an accident and risking the loss of life for myself and others.

I did have one vehicular accident of sorts. Shortly before I parted with my car keys, I was driving a golf cart through the parking lot at our country club. I encountered a very slow-moving vehicle whose driver had come to pick up another golfer. All I needed to do was to put my foot on the brake of the golf cart to allow him to pass. Unfortunately, my Parkinson's brain said to my foot, "Why don't you hit the accelerator instead." which was precisely what it did. I bumped into the car and proceeded to fall out of the golf cart. The only thing damaged was me, lots of abrasions and a broken nose. The result was a trip to the emergency room to clean me up and, two days later, a visit to an ENT doc to reset my broken nose. Since we had plans to join our daughter, her husband, and two grandchildren aboard a Disney cruise four days after the accident, I saw no reason to stay behind. A bandaged nose and lots of scratches and bruises, did cause me to stand out in a crowd. It was the perfect make up, however, for on-board pirate night!

So, What Now

In a phone conversation with my sister in California recently, after updating each other about our families, we launched into a discussion of our aches and pains. When we were in our 40s and 50s, we swore we would not follow in the footsteps of our parents and discuss, in detail, our health issues as we aged. I am quite certain that each generation professes the same intention, but promptly violates it as they approach Medicare age. Whether it is cancer, diabetes, heart abnormalities, breathing challenges, or mental decline, senior adults talk about what ails them. Sometimes, when overhearing conversations, one gets the impression that each person is trying to outdo the other by having something worse or lasting longer. Ask a young person how they are doing, and you'll probably get an answer such as "fine" or "doing great."

Ask a 70-year-old, and they are likely to be much more specific, telling you just exactly how they are. They talk about that which occupies their mind, and the process of aging is what they are familiar with. I was taught at a young age, if asked how I was doing, to simply say I'm doing fine. That was a polite way of greeting people who didn't want to hear about all your detailed health records. As we reach a certain point in our lives, we somehow feel the need to answer questions truthfully and include a few details. There is a need to know if a friend might be living with the same health issue that you are. Perhaps he or she has found a better treatment or remedy than you have. There is also comfort in knowing that you are not the only one dealing with a disease.

There are many facets to a diagnosis of Parkinson's disease. As indicated earlier, if you tried to explain the signs and symptoms of the disease to someone who asked, "How are you?", you could be in for a very lengthy conversation indeed. Until you understand why some of the characteristics of Parkinson's exist, it is difficult to give a detailed account to someone not living with the disease. Some symptoms simply make no sense, but we are discussing a condition affecting the human brain, which is capable of millions of functions and defies being easily understood in a simplistic manner. No two Parkinson's patients are alike. There are certain common characteristics that many who have the disease exhibit.

Still, trying to make sense of each idiosyncrasy can be most challenging. Why do some people get a diagnosis and live with the symptoms for 30 years while others are diagnosed and die within less than 10 years? What is the trigger that causes one to develop Parkinson's disease while others exposed to the same trigger do not?

Those Who Care

At some point, one realizes the need to have someone else assist with activities that were easily performed prior to a diagnosis of Parkinson's, whether that be daily living or special projects. Volumes have been written about caregiving, but a few practical points might make the introduction of a caregiver into one's life a bit easier.

Patience must be at the top of the list of suggestions for both the person with Parkinson's, as well as the caregiver. As we discussed earlier, over the years, life slows down concerning most everything that involves the diagnosed person. Build extra time into whatever project you are attempting. More time to get dressed, more time to shower, more time to navigate one's surroundings. Attempting to hurry only serves to slow the body down even more. The stress resulting from hurrying may cause you to take risks with your balance. Stress makes many of the symptoms worse as well. Tremor is especially susceptible to stress.

Flexibility on the part of both individuals to allow for

a change of plans, if necessary, reduces stress and disagreements. It is important to keep an open mind and be willing to change plans should fatigue or unexpected conditions come up.

Availability of medication at all times is advisable. Wearing a watch and having a small pillbox to hold meds, plus a water bottle, are all crucial. Keeping a water bottle and tiny bag of pills in your car always will reassure you that, should you need to take medication, you have what is necessary.

Know and understand one's limitations. Do not try to overdo, thus risking injury to oneself and others.

Stay informed and advocate for oneself. When possible, caregivers may want to attend doctors' visits along with the patient. Two sets of ears are always better than one.

Associate with individuals who lift you up, not with those who wear you down.

Take a walk, ride a bike, sing in the shower, learn a new dance, hit a punching bag, meet a friend for lunch, stroll down memory lane, swing a club, pot a geranium, write a book!

Keep moving! It is better to wear out than to rust.

You Will Not Die from Parkinson's

Shortly after being diagnosed, one of the first events that I attended was a class entitled Parkinson's 101. My husband and our adult daughter attended the class with me at our local chapter of the Parkinson's Foundation. After the hour-long class was over, I was practically in tears. Seeing so many people in wheelchairs or using walkers was not what I had expected. Our daughter, however, was elated because of one simple statement from the person leading the class. Her words, "You will not die from Parkinson's," was all that our daughter needed to hear to make her realize that I could live for a long time with this disease. Two different perspectives on the same gathering.

One thing is for certain, the number of cases of Parkinson's is increasing around the world. Perhaps more individuals are coming forward as they learn of the symptoms and treatments available. Perhaps the addition of chemicals and toxins of all sorts in the environment is causing the increase. Perhaps there is simply more awareness of the disease as the influence and availability of social media expands. Whatever the reason, the number of cases being reported is on the rise. Again, one does not die directly as a result of contracting the disease, but rather from one of the conditions caused by Parkinson's disease—falls from poor balance, choking from stiffening throat muscles, etc. With Agent Orange, death may result from some condition caused by the herbicide—cancer, heart disease, lung disease, etc.

There are many investigative studies underway to better determine who will develop the disease. Being able to diagnose Parkinson's earlier is at the heart of several ongoing projects. When you sense your first symptom, you have already lost 80% of the dopamine that you originally had. New medications are also the subject of much research in an attempt to make those of us living with Parkinson's enjoy a better standard of life. The possibility that Parkinson's may be tied to an irregularity in gene structure is at the forefront of still other research projects.

My hope in sharing my story is that others may realize that life can go on even while living with this chronic condition. It is not my intention to recommend new treatments or medications for the disease. Find a competent, knowledgeable movement disorder specialist or neurologist who can guide you through those issues. I simply wish to give hope to those who may be struggling, that life is still worth living to the fullest.

Less than one week ago, on my regular visit to my neurologist, I asked him why I was doing better than average managing my symptoms. His response was simple, "You have stayed active!"

Leaving a Legacy

When I'm gone and only a memory, what will they say of me?
I recycled wine bottles and composted my garbage.
I bought someone dinner and shared my dessert.
I smiled when I was hurting; gave hugs when they were needed.
I grew my own veggies and shared them with friends.
I wrote silly poems to help others heal.
I spoke of the war and gave praise to the wounded;
I honored the fallen, lest others might forget.
I voted for the candidate who could make a difference.
I made a donation to lift someone up.
I offered my time when others had little.
I called a sick neighbor and listened—just listened.
I shared my life's past that we might learn a lesson.
I worked this old body as hard as I could.
I did make a difference. I did leave my mark.

Acknowledgements

First and foremost, I must recognize my husband Jim, our son Matt and his wife Gen, our daughter Jen and her husband Matt, as well as my two grandchildren Will and Emma. They have walked with me on this Parkinson's journey for many years. I realize that my grandchildren have only known me as living with this disease. There was a time, before they were born, when I wasn't shaking or falling in my garden. They have been supportive and understanding through the ups and downs. They have all been willing to change some of their future plans in order to make accommodations for my lifestyle. This journey would have been much more difficult without a supportive family.

I need to recognize two wonderful organizations which have given hope and practical reinforcement to me and thousands of others, in dealing with PD and similar conditions. The first is Turning Point, the center for hope and healing, in Leawood, Kansas. The second is the Parkinson's Foundation, which offers support across the country. The classes and seminars offered by both groups strengthened my resilience over the last two decades.

Certain individuals deserve special recognition. Dr Irene Bettinger and Dr Raj Pahwa. Their medical advice has served me well through the years. Kudos to Caryn Mirriam-Goldberg and my fellow writers who continue to encourage putting pen to paper. Thank you to neighbors and friends, especially Judy Gleeson and Mary Lynn Clark, who have stepped forward to act as my chauffeur when I gave up the keys to my car. Your kindness has been greatly appreciated. Thank you to Susan, Mary, Moira, and Kim for being there. Daughter-in-law Gen has again graciously given of her time to edit my manuscript. To Bob Babcock and Deeds Publishing, thanks again.

Finally, to all people with Parkinson's, especially fellow Vietnam veterans, I wish you good health and a safe journey.

www.turningpointkc.org

www.parkinson.org

Louise (Lou) Graul Eisenbrandt

Growing up in a small Illinois town, Lou decided to join the Army to "see the world." After graduating as a Registered Nurse in June 1968, she attended basic training, then headed to Ft. Dix, New Jersey, her first duty assignment.

In September 1969, she received orders for Vietnam, arriving there on November 1. During her year at the 91st Evac Hospital in Chu Lai, she cared for GIs, South Vietnamese soldiers, and civilians, even Viet Cong and NVA soldiers. From malaria and hepatitis to double amputees, massive head traumas and deadly bullet wounds, Lt. Graul saw it all.

Her first book, *Vietnam Nurse, Mending and Remembering*, chronicled her experiences working as an Army nurse in a theater of war. She took us through the sights and sounds of combat nursing, waterskiing on the South China Sea, a weekend jeep trip with flak jackets and helmets, and surviving early-morning rocket attacks. The book was recognized with a silver medal award by the Military Writers Society of America in the Memoir category.

Her second book describes how a simple twitching finger in 2002, would lead her to be diagnosed with Parkinson's disease and change her life forever. Learning that Parkinson's was on the Veterans Administration list of conditions related to exposure to Agent Orange, she filed a successful claim for compensation.

For the past 40 years, the author has been sharing her experiences with students and community groups. She serves on the People with Parkinson's council of the national Parkinson's Foundation as well as the board of the Heartland chapter of the Parkinson's Foundation. She is Chairman Emerita of the board of Turning Point in Leawood, KS and a board member of the Veterans Voices Writing Project. She has been employed as a travel agent, children's cooking instructor, and stained-glass artisan. Her other interests are travel, photography, golf, gardening, and grand parenting.

She and husband Jim have two grown children, Jen and Matt. Both are married. She also has two grandchildren.

She can be contacted at: leisenbr@gmail.com

CPSIA information can be obtained
at www.ICGtesting.com
Printed in the USA
LVHW111348170422
716246LV00003B/7